With Jesus I Love

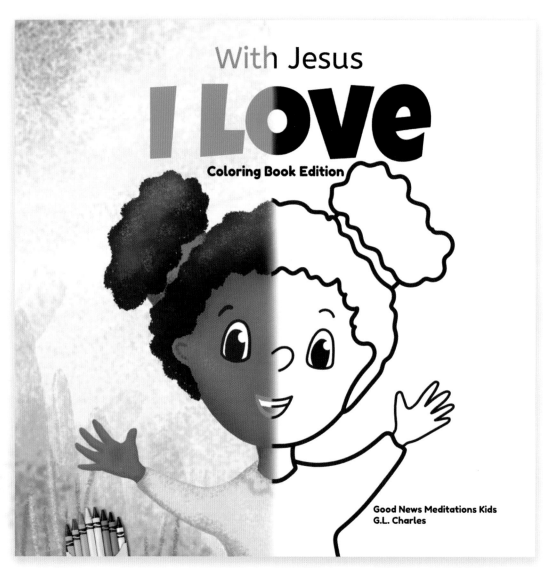

With Jesus

I Love

Coloring Book Edition

Good News Meditations Kids
G.L. Charles

To receive print-ready samples from the coloring book
version of this book, please go to gnmkids.com/free

This book belongs to :

_____

This is the story of a little girl called Grace. She lives in
a beautiful house with her mommy, her daddy,
and her little sister, Angel.

Grace loves spending time with her mommy because she always has so much fun and learns a lot of new things.

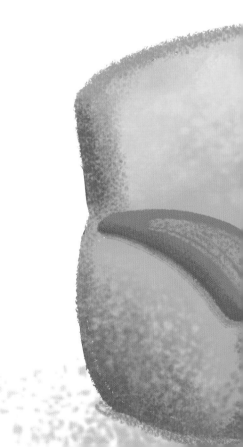

One night, Grace is sitting on her bed, crying. "Why are you crying, Grace?" asks Mommy.

"A girl from daycare is always very mean to me. I don't like her, Mommy!" Grace explains.

Mommy looks at Grace and says, "Grace, here in our house we always choose love. We love everybody, even the people who aren't always kind to us."

"Really?" answered Grace, her big brown eyes wide open. "But...but how do we do that? I don't think I can do it!"

"Well, Jesus has already filled your heart with the same love He has in His heart, my dear. He always helps you to love everybody, even those who have been mean to you. You just have to let his love shine through you!" Mommy explains.

"Wow, I didn't know that!" Grace exclaims. "When I see the little girl tomorrow, I'll tell her I'm not angry anymore because Jesus helps me to love her."

Mommy smiles and says, "That is wonderful! You are a true princess!"

Grace quietly says to herself, "Now I know that with Jesus, I can love!"

She is ready for tomorrow.

"...because the love of God is shed abroad in our hearts by the Holy Ghost which is given unto us."

• Romans 5:5 KJV

Author's note:

Thank you so much for reading this book. If you enjoyed this book, we would love it if you could leave a review and recommend it to a friend.

If there is anything you would like to share with us to help us improve this book, please go to gnmkids.com/feedback

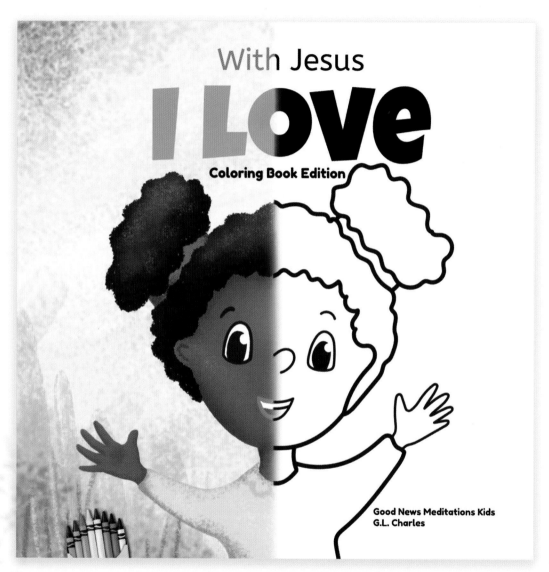

With Jesus
I Love
Coloring Book Edition

Good News Meditations Kids
G.L. Charles

To receive print-ready samples from the coloring book version of this book, please go to gnmkids.com/free

Please checkout our other books:

gnmkids.com